TOP SECRET!

THIS DIARY
BELONGS TO:

....

KEEP OUT!

DAN ◆ TDM

Diary & Activity Book 2017

THIS EDITION FIRST PUBLISHED IN GREAT BRITAIN IN 2016 BY
TRAPEZE
AN IMPRINT OF THE ORION PUBLISHING GROUP LTD
CARMELITE HOUSE
50 VICTORIA EMBANKMENT
LONDON EC4Y 0DZ
AN HACHETTE UK COMPANY

DESIGNED BY US-NOW.COM

3 5 7 9 10 8 6 4 2

A CIP CATALOGUE RECORD FOR THIS BOOK IS AVAILABLE FROM THE BRITISH LIBRARY.

ISBN: 978 1 4091 7118 8

PRINTED IN ITALY

EVERY EFFORT HAS BEEN MADE TO FULFIL REQUIREMENTS WITH REGARD TO
REPRODUCING COPYRIGHT MATERIAL. THE AUTHOR AND PUBLISHER WILL BE
GLAD TO RECTIFY ANY OMISSIONS AT THE EARLIEST OPPORTUNITY.

WWW.ORIONBOOKS.CO.UK

FSC
www.fsc.org

MIX
Paper from
responsible sources
FSC® C023419

DAN ◆ TDM

Diary & Activity Book 2017

Loads of things to make & do!

HI EVERYONE, DANTDM HERE AND WELCOME TO MY 2017 DIARY!

2016 WAS AN AMAZING YEAR -- I WROTE MY FIRST GRAPHIC NOVEL, I GOT TO TRAVEL ALL OVER THE WORLD AND MEET LOADS OF YOU ON MY TOUR, I HIT OVER 12 MILLION SUBSCRIBERS ON MY YOUTUBE CHANNEL, AND, MOST IMPORTANTLY, I GOT TO SPEND THE YEAR DOING WHAT I LOVE MOST: CREATING VIDEOS AND SHARING THEM WITH YOU ALL! ALL OF THIS WAS THANKS TO YOU GUYS. YOUR INCREDIBLE SUPPORT IN WATCHING, LIKING, AND INTERACTING WITH MY VIDEOS HAS MADE ALL THIS POSSIBLE AND I'M SO EXCITED TO SEE WHAT 2017 HAS IN STORE!

SO, BUCKLE UP AND JOIN ME ON AN ADVENTURE THROUGH THE YEAR AHEAD! THIS DIARY HAS LOADS OF ROOM FOR YOU TO FILL IN YOUR IMPORTANT DATES, AND IT'S JAM PACKED WITH QUIZZES, PUZZLES, CHALLENGES AND FUN EXPERIMENTS TO KEEP YOU ENTERTAINED ALL YEAR LONG.

LET'S SEE IF WE CAN MAKE THIS YEAR THE BEST ONE YET!

ABOUT YOU

NAME: ....

AGE: ....

TWITTER: ....

SNAPCHAT: ....

INSTAGRAM: ....

HIDDEN IN THE PAGES OF

5 X ENCHANTED CRYSTALS

6 X 'P' GUNS

2 X GRIMS

THIS DIARY YOU WILL FIND:

7 X
CRYSTAL
NECKLACES

1 X
SCANNER

4 X
SWORDS

3 X
PIGS

ACTIVITY: NEW YEAR'S RESOLUTIONS

DAN AND TRAYAURUS HAVE MADE A LIST OF THEIR TOP 5 RESOLUTIONS FOR THE YEAR AHEAD. WRITE YOUR LIST!

DAN:

1. EAT MORE APPLES AND FEWER COOKIES!
2. TRAVEL TO NEW PLACES
3. MAKE MORE AWESOME VIDEOS
4. PLAY MORE VIDEO GAMES
5. TRY ICED TEA FOR THE FIRST TIME

TRAYAURUS:

1. BE LESS CLUMSY
2. EAT MORE SANDWICHES
3. BUY NEW SHOES AND A NEW LAB COAT
4. TRY NOT TO BREAK LAPTOP THIS YEAR!
5. GROW MORE HAIR...

YOUR RESOLUTIONS:

1.

2.

3.

4.

5.

MON 26TH BOXING DAY

TUES 27TH

WEDS 28TH

THURS 29TH

FRI 30TH

SAT 31ST NEW YEAR'S EVE

SUN 1ST NEW YEAR'S DAY

DAN TDM

FULL NAME:
DANIEL MIDDLETON

DATE OF BIRTH:
8TH NOVEMBER 1991

STARTED YOUTUBE:
14TH JULY 2012

FAVOURITE COLOUR:
BLUE

FIRST VIDEO:
SHELVES MOD

FAVOURITE COMPUTER GAME:
MINECRAFT

YOUR FAVOURITE VIDEO:
FIVE SECRETS
ABOUT DANTDM

MON 2ND UK BANK HOLIDAY

TUES 3RD

WEDS 4TH

THURS 5TH

FRI 6TH

SAT 7TH

SUN 8TH

ACTIVITY: INVISIBLE WRITING

EVER WANTED TO SEND A SECRET LETTER?
NOW YOU CAN WITH THIS INVISIBLE INK!

YOU WILL NEED:

- LEMON JUICE IN A CONTAINER (EITHER FRESH OR BOTTLED)
- A PAINTBRUSH OR COTTON BUD
- PAPER

INSTRUCTIONS:

1. USE THE 'INK' BY DIPPING YOUR PAINTBRUSH OR STICK INTO THE LEMON JUICE

2. WRITE YOUR SECRET MESSAGE

3. ALLOW THE PAPER TO DRY, THEN SEND IT TO THE RECIPIENT!

4. TO READ YOUR INVISIBLE LETTER, HOLD THE PAPER UP TO SUNLIGHT OR USE A HAIRDRYER TO MAKE THE MESSAGE APPEAR!

5. THE HEAT WILL CAUSE THE WRITING TO TURN PALE BROWN SO THAT YOU CAN READ IT.

6. AN ALTERNATIVE METHOD IS TO SPRINKLE A SMALL AMOUNT OF SALT OVER THE LEMON JUICE BEFORE IT DRIES. AFTER A MINUTE, WIPE IT OFF AND COLOUR OVER THE PAPER WITH A WAX CRAYON TO REVEAL THE MESSAGE!

JANUARY

WEEK 3

MON 9TH

TUES 10TH

WEDS 11TH

THURS 12TH

FRI 13TH

SAT 14TH

SUN 15TH

ACTIVITY: WORDSEARCH

```
D F J L G B C W V T H P A Q W V E
P I O R N O T N E D F I M A J F S
L T A X M P R M O A H G I V K W C
F S W M G C G I Z M O C N O D E L
U I E C O R S U R V G E E J A G A
G V H U I N O N T J D I C S R L T
Y J Q V P E D V E U B Q R G C Q S
B P S Z L F T L R I C N A M I K Y
O X T R A Y A U R U S T F L E A R
C I H E H R M C A N D O T L B B C
V B D P C L E B N S I R V D S T W
S D A N T D M P C R E E L L I E G
N B E T F M C S E Y D N A M T E H
O S I Y E R J F L S M I R G X I K
T R A C E N I M A D O F E V T R O
D B Z N L Q R A I X Z C A I D P I
```

DANTDM	GRIM	MINECART
MINECRAFT	GIZMO	CRYSTAL
TRAYAURUS	TERRANCE	ELLIE
DENTON	DIAMOND	DARCIE

ANSWERS ON PAGE 119

MON 16TH

TUES 17TH

WEDS 18TH

THURS 19TH

FRI 20TH

SAT 21ST

SUN 22ND

TIME TO EXPERIMENT

UH OH – DAN AND TRAYAURUS' MOST RECENT EXPERIMENT HAS GONE HORRIBLY WRONG. WHAT WAS MEANT TO BE A CUTE PET TURNED INTO A PINK SLIME MONSTER! PERHAPS YOU CAN DO BETTER -- FILL IN THE INGREDIENTS FOR YOUR VERY OWN EXPERIMENT:

MIX FIVE PARTS .... WITH TWO PARTS.....................

ADD HAIR OF............................ STIR IN ....

HEAT AT .... DEGREES

ADD THE CHEMICAL COMPOUND ....

TRANSFER THE MIXTURE TO THE ....

WAIT FOR .... MINUTES AND YOU WILL HAVE MADE

....

MON 23RD

___

TUES 24TH

___

WEDS 25TH

___

THURS 26TH

___

FRI 27TH

___

SAT 28TH

SUN 29TH

ACTIVITY: DOT-TO-DOT

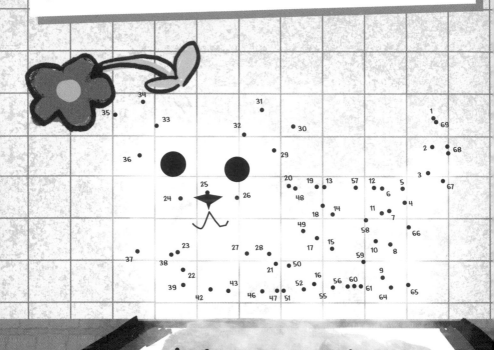

COMPLETE THE DOT-TO-DOT TO FIND OUT WHO LOVES STOMPING IN THE DEBRIS OF A 'P' GUN DEMONSTRATION.

MON 30TH

TUES 31ST

WEDS 1ST FEBRUARY

THURS 2ND

FRI 3RD

SAT 4TH

SUN 5TH

MON 6TH WAITANGI DAY (NEW ZEALAND)

___

TUES 7TH

___

WEDS 8TH

___

THURS 9TH

___

FRI 10TH

___

SAT 11TH

SUN 12TH

MON 13TH

TUES 14TH VALENTINE'S DAY

WEDS 15TH

THURS 16TH

FRI 17TH

SAT 18TH

SUN 19TH

MAZE

START

HELP DAN THROUGH THE MAZE TO REACH THE CRYSTAL
-- BUT BEWARE OF DENTON'S CLONES! ANSWER ON PAGE 119

FINISH

FEBRUARY

MON 20TH

TUES 21ST

WEDS 22ND

THURS 23RD

FRI 24TH

SAT 25TH

SUN 26TH

MON 27TH

TUES 28TH SHROVE TUESDAY

WEDS 1ST MARCH ASH WEDNESDAY   ST DAVID'S DAY

THURS 2ND

FRI 3RD

SAT 4TH

SUN 5TH

DR. TRAYAURUS

FUN FACTS

FULL NAME:
DR. TRAYAURUS

DATE OF BIRTH:
IT'S A SECRET!

BEST FRIEND:
DANTDM

OCCUPATION:
PROFESSIONAL SCIENTIST

FAVOURITE HOBBY:
SCIENCE!!

FAVOURITE EXPERIMENT:
THE TIME I TURNED EVERY PLAYER INTO A VILLAGER

WORST EXPERIMENT:
WHEN I ACCIDENTALLY TURNED GRIM INTO A SKELETON

FAVOURITE FOOD:
SANDWICHES, SANDWICHES, SANDWICHES!

IF YOU WEREN'T A SCIENTIST, YOU'D BE:
A COMPETITIVE SPEED-EATER

MON 6TH

TUES 7TH

WEDS 8TH

THURS 9TH

FRI 10TH

SAT 11TH

SUN 12TH

ACTIVITY: CROSSWORD

ACROSS
3. DANTDM'S SCIENTIST FRIEND
4. A SCIENTIFIC TEST
7. DANTDM'S FAVOURITE GAME
8. DANTDM'S ENEMY

DOWN
1. DANTDM'S FAVOURITE VIDEO WEBSITE
2. PLACE FOR CONDUCTING SCIENTIFIC EXPERIMENTS
5. ANIMAL THAT LIKES MUD
6. SHINY, PRECIOUS GEM

MON 13TH

TUES 14TH

WEDS 15TH

THURS 16TH

FRI 17TH ST. PATRICK'S DAY

SAT 18TH

SUN 19TH

❀ Mother's Day! ❀

MUMS ARE SO SPECIAL, AND SOMETIMES WE CAN
FORGET TO SHOW THEM HOW MUCH WE CARE. HERE
ARE TEN WAYS YOU CAN SHOW YOUR MUM HOW MUCH
YOU LOVE THEM ON MOTHER'S DAY!

1. MAKE HER BREAKFAST IN BED, BUT NOT TOO EARLY --
   SHE DESERVES A LIE IN!

2. MAKE HER A HOMEMADE CARD

3. TIDY YOUR ROOM

4. GIVE HER A HEAD MASSAGE

5. PICK SOME FLOWERS FROM THE GARDEN AND PUT THEM
   IN A VASE ON THE KITCHEN TABLE

6. GET A PACK OF CARDS AND WRITE ON THE BACK OF EACH
   ONE THE 52 REASONS WHY YOU LOVE HER!

7. DON'T FIGHT WITH YOUR SIBLINGS

8. LET HER WATCH HER FAVOURITE SHOWS ON TV

9. OFFER TO WASH THE DISHES

10. PUT YOUR COMPUTER/PHONE AWAY -- SHE'D LOVE TO
    SPEND TIME WITH YOU, NOT YOUR SCREEN

MON 20TH

_____

TUES 21ST

_____

WEDS 22ND

_____

THURS 23RD

_____

FRI 24TH

_____

SAT 25TH

SUN 26TH MOTHER'S DAY

APRIL FOOL'S DAY

PRANK YOUR PARENTS WITH THESE
AWESOME APRIL FOOL'S DAY PRANKS!

1. STUFF THE TOE OF THEIR SHOES WITH TOILET PAPER, AND WATCH THEM TRY TO GET THEM ON IN THE MORNING!

2. SELLOTAPE A PARTY POPPER TO THEIR BEDROOM DOOR -- THAT'LL WAKE THEM UP WITH A **BANG!**

3. PUT A FEW DROPS OF FOOD COLOURING IN THE BOTTOM OF THEIR CEREAL BOWL, THEN COVER IT WITH CEREAL. WHEN THEY POUR THE MILK IT WILL CHANGE COLOUR AS IT RISES TO THE TOP...

4. COVER THE REMOTE CONTROL SENSOR WITH A PIECE OF TAPE.

5. PAINT A BAR OF SOAP WITH CLEAR NAIL POLISH AND LEAVE IT IN THE SHOWER. THE SOAP WON'T LATHER, WHICH WILL MAKE THEM GO CRAZY AS THEY GET READY FOR WORK!

MON 27TH

TUES 28TH

WEDS 29TH

THURS 30TH

FRI 31ST

SAT 1ST APRIL FOOL'S DAY

SUN 2ND APRIL

Pigs in Mud Cakes

PREP TIME: 20 MINS / SERVINGS: 12

INGREDIENTS:

2 LARGE BARS OF CHOCOLATE, BROKEN INTO PIECES
2 TBSP GOLDEN SYRUP
50G BUTTER

75G/3OZ CORNFLAKES/SHREDDED WHEAT/PUFFED RICE CEREAL
36 MINI CHOCOLATE EGGS
PIG SHAPED GUMMY SWEETS

1. LINE A 12 HOLE CAKE TIN WITH PAPER CUPCAKE CASES

2. MELT THE CHOCOLATE, GOLDEN SYRUP AND BUTTER IN A MICROWAVE-SAFE BOWL IN THE MICROWAVE, STIRRING THE MIXTURE UNTIL SMOOTH (RECRUIT A GROWN UP TO HELP YOU!)

3. CAREFULLY STIR IN THE CORNFLAKES UNTIL THE CEREAL IS COATED IN THE CHOCOLATE

4. DIVIDE THE MIXTURE BETWEEN THE PAPER CASES AND PRESS YOUR PIG SHAPED SWEETS INTO THE CENTRE OF EACH NEST.

5. CHILL IN THE FRIDGE FOR 1 HOUR, OR UNTIL COMPLETELY SET.

6. EAT!

APRIL

WEEK 15

MON 3RD

TUES 4TH

WEDS 5TH

THURS 6TH

FRI 7TH

SAT 8TH

SUN 9TH

EASTER!

IT'S EASTER, ONE OF MY FAVOURITE
TIMES OF YEAR, AND TO CELEBRATE YOU CAN DECORATE
YOUR OWN DANTDM EGGS. EITHER DRAW YOUR FAVOURITE
CHARACTERS ONTO THE EGGS BELOW, OR COME UP
WITH YOUR OWN DESIGNS!

MON 10TH

TUES 11TH

WEDS 12TH

THURS 13TH

FRI 14TH GOOD FRIDAY

SAT 15TH

SUN 16TH EASTER SUNDAY

MON 17TH EASTER MONDAY

TUES 18TH

WEDS 19TH

THURS 20TH

FRI 21ST

SAT 22ND

SUN 23RD ST GEORGE'S DAY

MON 24TH

TUES 25TH ANZAC DAY (AUSTRALIA & NEW ZEALAND)

WEDS 26TH

THURS 27TH

FRI 28TH

SAT 29TH

SUN 30TH

BANK HOLIDAY!

DAN AND TRAYAURUS' LAB IS IN A RIGHT OLD MESS.
THERE ARE MACHINES, TOP SECRET PAPERS, LEFTOVER
EXPERIMENTS AND OTHER BITS AND BOBS EVERYWHERE!
THEY'RE GOING TO SPEND THEIR BANK HOLIDAY TIDYING
UP. WHY DON'T YOU GET INVOLVED? WRITE YOUR OWN TO-
DO LIST IN THE SPACE BELOW.

TO DO:

1. ....
2. ....
3. ....
4. ....
5. ....
6. ....
7. ....
8. ....
9. ....
10. ....

MON 1ST UK BANK HOLIDAY

_____

TUES 2ND

_____

WEDS 3RD

_____

THURS 4TH

_____

FRI 5TH

_____

SAT 6TH

SUN 7TH

DENTON HAS USED THE POWER OF THE ENCHANTED CRYSTAL TO CREATE TERRIFYING CLONES! CAN YOU SPOT THE TEN DIFFERENCES BETWEEN THESE TWO SCENES FROM WITHIN DENTON'S LAB? ANSWERS ON PAGE 119.

MON 8TH

TUES 9TH

WEDS 10TH

THURS 11TH

FRI 12TH

SAT 13TH

SUN 14TH MOTHER'S DAY
(AUSTRALIA & NEW ZEALAND)

MON 15TH

TUES 16TH

WEDS 17TH

THURS 18TH

FRI 19TH

SAT 20TH

SUN 21ST

MY FAVOURITE VIDEOS

HI GUYS, I'VE HAD SO MUCH FUN MAKING VIDEOS FOR YOU OVER THE PAST FEW YEARS, AND THANK YOU ALL SO MUCH FOR WATCHING! BELOW IS A LIST OF MY TOP 5 VIDEOS -- WHICH ARE YOUR FAVOURITES?

DAN'S TOP 5 FAVOURITE VIDEOS:

1. FIVE SECRETS ABOUT DANTDM

2. HOW I MET DR TRAYAURUS

3. FIVE SECRETS ABOUT DR TRAYAURUS

4. DR TRAYAURUS GOES TO PRISON

5. DANTDM GETS SICK!!

YOUR TOP 5 FAVOURITE VIDEOS:

1. ....

2. ....

3. ....

4. ....

5. ....

MON 22ND

TUES 23RD

WEDS 24TH

THURS 25TH

FRI 26TH

SAT 27TH

SUN 28TH

DANTDM Q&A

YOU GUYS SENT ME LOADS OF
AMAZING QUESTIONS IN MY TWITTER Q&A!
HERE ARE SOME OF MY ANSWERS...

1. WHAT INSPIRED YOU TO START YOUTUBE?

I'VE ALWAYS BEEN REALLY CREATIVE AND LOVED MAKING VIDEOS, SO YOUTUBE WAS THE PERFECT OUTLET FOR ME.

2. HOW LONG DOES IT TAKE TO MAKE A VIDEO?

BETWEEN 3-5 HOURS PER VIDEO FROM START TO FINISH. SOME HAVE TAKEN ME MUCH LONGER THOUGH!

3. HOW DID YOU COME UP WITH YOUR YOUTUBE CHANNEL NAME?

SIMPLY, I PUT MY TWO FAVOURITE MINECRAFT ITEMS TOGETHER, DIAMONDS AND MINECARTS!

4. WHO WAS YOUR CHILDHOOD HERO?

SONIC THE HEDGEHOG.

5. WHAT IS YOUR FAVOURITE PART OF YOUR JOB?

BEING ABLE TO DO SOMETHING I LOVE EVERY SINGLE DAY.

6. IF YOU WEREN'T A YOUTUBER, WHAT WOULD YOUR IDEAL JOB BE?

MUSIC PRODUCER.

7. DO YOU HAVE ANY BROTHERS OR SISTERS?

I HAVE ONE YOUNGER BROTHER!

8. WHAT WAS YOUR FIRST VIDEO ABOUT?

MY FIRST EVER VIDEO WAS OPENING PACKS OF POKEMON CARDS!

9. WHO ARE YOUR FAVOURITE YOUTUBERS?

THNXCYA AND THINKNOODLES!

10. IF YOU COULD GO BACK IN TIME, WHERE WOULD YOU GO AND WHAT WOULD YOU DO?

I WOULD GO BACK TO WHEN DINOSAURS RULED THE EARTH AND SEE HOW LONG I COULD SURVIVE!

11. WHAT IS YOUR FAVOURITE FOOD?

PIZZA.

12. IF YOU GOT ANOTHER PUG, WHAT WOULD YOU CALL IT?

KANYE.

13. IF YOU COULD BRING A FILM/GAME/ COMIC BOOK CHARACTER TO LIFE, WHO WOULD IT BE AND WHY?

SPIDERMAN SO THAT HE COULD TEACH ME HOW TO WEB SLING. THAT WOULD SAVE A LOT OF TIME!

14. WHAT IS YOUR FAVOURITE HOBBY, APART FROM GAMING?

PLAYING, RECORDING AND WRITING MUSIC.

MON 29TH SPRING BANK HOLIDAY

_____

TUES 30TH

_____

WEDS 31ST

_____

THURS 1ST JUNE

_____

FRI 2ND

_____

SAT 3RD

SUN 4TH

ACTIVITY:
NEW YEAR'S RESOLUTIONS
PROGRESS CHECK

OK, GUYS, WE'RE HALFWAY THROUGH THE YEAR SO IT'S TIME TO CHECK HOW YOU'RE DOING ON COMPLETING YOUR NEW YEAR'S RESOLUTIONS. FLICK BACK TO PAGE 10 AND MARK YOUR PROGRESS USING THE LIST BELOW. FILL OUT WHAT YOU NEED TO DO TO ENSURE YOU GET A GOLD STAR AT THE END OF THE YEAR!

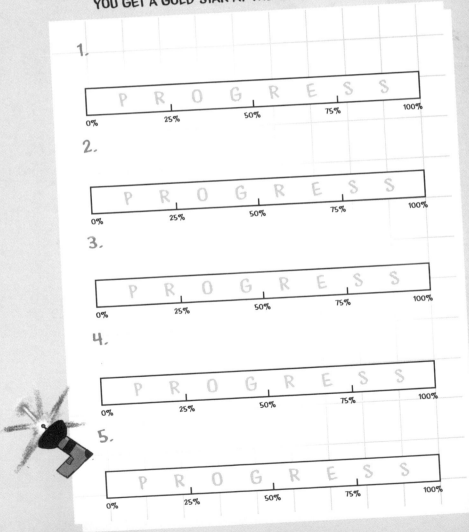

1.

PROGRESS

0%   25%   50%   75%   100%

2.

PROGRESS

0%   25%   50%   75%   100%

3.

PROGRESS

0%   25%   50%   75%   100%

4.

PROGRESS

0%   25%   50%   75%   100%

5.

PROGRESS

0%   25%   50%   75%   100%

MON 5TH

TUES 6TH

WEDS 7TH

THURS 8TH

FRI 9TH

SAT 10TH

SUN 11TH

FATHER'S DAY!

SHOW YOUR DAD HOW MUCH YOU LOVE HIM, BY MAKING HIM THIS EXPLODING **BATH BOMB!** HE'LL HAVE A RIOT THE NEXT TIME HE TAKES A BATH...

YOU WILL NEED:

2 X CUPS OF BICARBONATE OF SODA
1 X CUP OF CREAM OF TARTAR
1 TSP FOOD COLOURING
2 TSP FOOD FLAVOURING
ICE CUBE OR COOKIE TRAY
SPRITZER OR SPRAY BOTTLE WITH WATER INSIDE

METHOD:

1. MIX THE CREAM OF TARTAR AND THE BICARBONATE OF SODA IN A BOWL WITH YOUR FINGERS.

2. ADD THE FOOD COLOURING AND FOOD FLAVOURING TO THE BOWL AND MIX USING YOUR HANDS. THE MIXTURE MAY BECOME LUMPY, BUT YOU CAN TURN IT BACK INTO POWDER BY RUBBING THE LUMPS.

3. USING THE SPRITZER OR SPRAY BOTTLE, SPRAY SOME WATER ONTO THE MIXTURE AND KEEP MIXING IT TOGETHER. YOU ONLY NEED A SMALL AMOUNT, SO ADD A LITTLE BIT AT A TIME.

4. SPOON THE MIXTURE INTO YOUR ICE CUBE TRAY OR COOKIE MOULDS AND PRESS DOWN WITH YOUR FINGERS. LEAVE TO DRY SOMEWHERE WARM AND DRY OVERNIGHT.

5. GENTLY REMOVE THEM FROM THE MOULD AND KEEP IN A BOX READY FOR YOUR DAD'S NEXT BATH! REMEMBER TO USE THEM WITHIN A FEW WEEKS, OTHERWISE THEY WILL LOSE THEIR FIZZ.

MON 12TH

TUES 13TH

WEDS 14TH

THURS 15TH

FRI 16TH

SAT 17TH

SUN 18TH FATHER'S DAY

ACTIVITY: BOUNCING EGGS

THIS EXPERIMENT IS FUN BUT CAN BE A LITTLE MESSY -- MAKE SURE YOU HAVE THE PERMISSION OF A RESPONSIBLE ADULT!

YOU WILL NEED:

- RAW EGGS (WHOLE)
- WHITE VINEGAR
- CLEAR JARS OR CONTAINERS, IDEALLY WITH A LID
- FOOD COLOURING

INSTRUCTIONS:

1. CAREFULLY PLACE YOUR EGG INTO A TALL, CLEAR CONTAINER WITH A WIDE MOUTH. THE EGG WILL EXPAND OVER TIME, SO MAKE SURE YOU HAVE SOME ROOM TO GET IT OUT AGAIN!

2. NEXT, COVER YOUR EGG WITH WHITE VINEGAR AND ADD A FEW DROPS OF FOOD COLOURING.

3. LEAVE FOR 3 DAYS, THEN GENTLY LIFT THE EGG OUT. THE SHELL SHOULD COME OFF EASILY, BUT BE VERY CAREFUL -- IF YOU SCRATCH THE MEMBRANE OF THE EGG, IT WILL BURST!

4. WHEN ALL THE SHELL IS REMOVED, GENTLY RINSE THE EGG UNDER THE TAP. DON'T TURN THE WATER ON TOO STRONG, OR YOU MIGHT BURST THE EGG!

5. YOU CAN NOW TEST YOUR EGG TO SEE IF IT WILL BOUNCE! DROP THE EGG FROM A HEIGHT OF 10-15CM -- ANY HIGHER AND YOUR EGG MIGHT SPLAT! IT'S BEST TO DO THIS IN A PYREX DISH OR OVEN TRAY, AND COVER YOUR WORK SURFACE TO AVOID MESS!

6. DON'T FORGET TO THROW YOUR EGG AWAY WHEN YOU'VE FINISHED PLAYING WITH IT! DEFINITELY DON'T EAT IT!

MON 19TH

TUES 20TH

WEDS 21ST

THURS 22ND

FRI 23RD

SAT 24TH

SUN 25TH

ACTIVITY: SUDOKU

9	4	7	2	6	8	1	5	3
		5	4		7	6	2	9
	6	3	9	5	1		8	7
1	3	2	7				9	6
				9		8		1
7	8	9					3	
	9	1	5	2	6		4	8
		8	1			9		2
4	2		8	7	9		1	5

GET YOUR BRAIN IN GEAR BY COMPLETING THIS SUDOKU
PUZZLE. FILL IN THE EMPTY SQUARES SO THAT THE
NUMBERS 1–9 APPEAR IN EACH ROW, COLUMN AND 3X3
BOX ONLY ONCE. ANSWER ON PAGE 120

MON 26TH

_____

TUES 27TH

_____

WEDS 28TH

_____

THURS 29TH

_____

FRI 30TH

_____

SAT 1ST JULY | SUN 2ND

DANTDM'S TOP 5 TIPS FOR STARTING YOUR OWN YOUTUBE CHANNEL

I ALWAYS GET ASKED, 'HOW DID YOU GET STARTED ON YOUTUBE?'. THE TRUTH IS THAT I DIDN'T REALLY KNOW WHAT I WAS DOING, AND JUST TRIED OUT DIFFERENT THINGS UNTIL I STARTED TO LEARN WHAT WORKED AND WHAT DIDN'T. OF COURSE, I'VE BEEN DOING IT FOR A LONG TIME NOW, SO HERE ARE MY TOP TIPS TO HELP YOU START YOUR OWN CHANNEL:

1. PRACTICE MAKES PERFECT -- YOUR FIRST VIDEO MIGHT NOT BE PERFECT, BUT THE MORE YOU MAKE, THE BETTER THEY'LL GET!

2. LOVE WHAT YOU DO! MAKING VIDEOS IS FUN. IF YOU LOVE WHAT YOU'RE DOING THEN OTHERS WILL TOO!

3. BE PATIENT! GROWING A CHANNEL TAKES TIME.

4. CHOOSE A SCHEDULE THAT WORKS FOR YOU AND BE CONSISTENT.

5. HAVE FUN!

MON 3RD

TUES 4TH

WEDS 5TH

THURS 6TH

FRI 7TH

SAT 8TH

SUN 9TH

MON 10TH

TUES 11TH

WEDS 12TH BANK HOLIDAY (IRELAND)

THURS 13TH

FRI 14TH

SAT 15TH

SUN 16TH

MON 17TH

TUES 18TH

WEDS 19TH

THURS 20TH

FRI 21ST

SAT 22ND

SUN 23RD

SCHOOL'S OUT

YAY! NO MORE SCHOOL UNTIL THE AUTUMN!
P-A-R-T-Y! MAKE A LIST OF ALL THE FUN STUFF
YOU'RE GOING TO DO WITH YOUR TIME OUT.

TO DO:

1. ....

2. ....

3. ....

4. ....

5. ....

6. ....

7. ....

8. ....

9. ....

10. ....

MON 24TH

TUES 25TH

WEDS 26TH

THURS 27TH

FRI 28TH

SAT 29TH

SUN 30TH

MAKE YOUR OWN VIDEO CHALLENGE!

WITH ALL THIS EXTRA TIME ON YOUR HANDS, YOU CAN GET STARTED ON YOUR OWN YOUTUBE CHANNEL. GRAB A VIDEO CAMERA OR USE A PHONE AND GET RECORDING. MAKE SURE YOU CHECK OUT MY TOP TIPS ON PAGE 60 AND TWEET ME THE LINK TO YOUR CHANNEL @DANTDM. WHO KNOWS, YOU COULD BE THE NEXT BIG YOUTUBE STAR!

IDEAS:

....

....

....

....

....

MON 31ST

TUES 1ST AUGUST

WEDS 2ND

THURS 3RD

FRI 4TH

SAT 5TH

SUN 6TH

ACTIVITY:

WORD JUMBLE

MIX UP THE LETTERS IN:

'DIAMOND MINECART'

TO MAKE AS MANY FOUR-LETTER WORDS AS POSSIBLE. TO GIVE YOU A CLUE, THERE ARE MORE THAN 70 POSSIBLE COMBINATIONS!

MON 7TH SUMMER BANK HOLIDAY (SCOTLAND)

TUES 8TH

WEDS 9TH

THURS 10TH

FRI 11TH

SAT 12TH

SUN 13TH

COMPLETE THE DOT-TO-DOT TO FIND OUT WHAT KIND OF PET TRAYAURUS USED TO OWN.

WOULD YOU RATHER...?

WOULD YOU RATHER... FILL IN YOUR ANSWERS AFTER DAN'S

HAVE SMELLY FEET OR BAD BREATH?
EWW! SMELLY FEET! |..|

NEVER HAVE TO SHOWER OR NEVER HAVE TO BRUSH YOUR
TEETH AGAIN?
NEVER HAVE TO SHOWER |..|

EAT SNUGS OR SNAILS?
GROSS...I'D EAT SLUGS. LESS CRUNCHY. |..|

LICK YOUR SHOE OR EAT YOUR SNOT?
EAT SNOT! |..|

TO ONLY BE ABLE TO WHISPER, OR ONLY ABLE TO SHOUT?
WHISPER! |..|

TELL YOUR TEACHER YOU LOVE THEM, OR BREAK
WIND IN CLASS?
BREAK WIND IN CLASS! |..|

BE SUPER STRONG OR SUPER FAST?
I'D BE SUPER FAST! |..|

HAVE THE ABILITY TO FLY OR BE INVISIBLE?
FLY, EVERY TIME. |..|

ALWAYS HAVE TO SAY EVERYTHING YOU'RE THINKING,
OR NEVER SPEAK AGAIN?
I'D NEVER SPEAK AGAIN. |..|

JUMP INTO A POOL OF CHOCOLATE ICE CREAM
OR A POOL OF PIZZA?
ICE CREAM!! YUM! |..|

MON 14TH

TUES 15TH

WEDS 16TH

THURS 17TH

FRI 18TH

SAT 19TH

SUN 20TH

GRIM

FUN FACTS

FULL NAME:
GRIM THE DOG

DATE OF BIRTH:
8TH NOVEMBER 2006

BEST FRIEND:
DANTDM

ENEMY:
BATH TIME

MOST LOVES:
BELLY RUBS

MOST HATES:
SWIMMING

FAVOURITE FOOD:
COOKED CHICKEN

MON 21ST

TUES 22ND

WEDS 23RD

THURS 24TH

FRI 25TH

SAT 26TH

SUN 27TH

ACTIVITY: WORDSEARCH

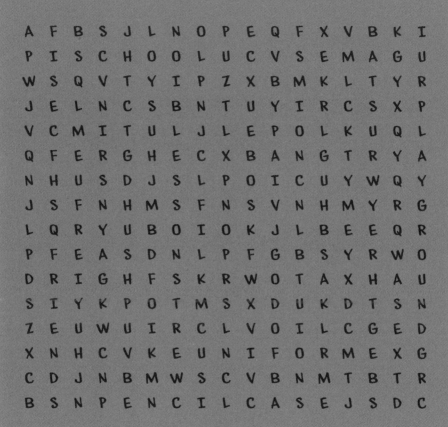

```
A F B S J L N O P E Q F X V B K I
P I S C H O O L U C V S E M A G U
W S Q V T Y I P Z X B M K L T Y R
J E L N C S B N T U Y I R C S X P
V C M I T U L J L E P O L K U Q L
Q F E R G H E C X B A N G T R Y A
N H U S D J S L P O I C U Y W Q Y
J S F N H M S F N S V N H M Y R G
L Q R Y U B O I O K J L B E E Q R
P F E A S D N L P F G B S Y R W O
D R I G H F S K R W O T A X H A U
S I Y K P O T M S X D U K D T S N
Z E U W U I R C L V O I L C G E D
X N H C V K E U N I F O R M E X G
C D J N B M W S C V B N M T B T R
B S N P E N C I L C A S E J S D C
```

SCHOOL   TEACHER   LESSONS
PENCILCASE   FRIENDS   GAMES
UNIFORM   PLAYGROUND   FUN

ANSWERS ON PAGE 119

MON 28TH SUMMER BANK HOLIDAY (UK)

TUES 29TH

WEDS 30TH

THURS 31ST

FRI 1ST SEPTEMBER

SAT 2ND

SUN 3RD FATHER'S DAY
(AUSTRALIA & NEW ZEALAND)

BACK TO SCHOOL!

THE NEW TERM HAS STARTED AND IT'S TIME TO GET BACK TO SCHOOL. DRAW YOUR IDEAL SCHOOL UNIFORM ON TO THE FIGURES OF DAN AND TRAYAURUS BELOW.

MON 4TH

TUES 5TH

WEDS 6TH

THURS 7TH

FRI 8TH

SAT 9TH

SUN 10TH

TIME TO EXPERIMENT

BE THE ENVY OF YOUR CLASSMATES BY
MAKING THIS AWESOME SLIME!

YOU WILL NEED:

PVA GLUE
FOOD COLOURING
TALCUM POWDER/
BABY POWDER

SOME OLD NEWSPAPERS
TO PROTECT THE SURFACE
YOU'RE WORKING ON

METHOD:

1. ADD APPROX. 6 TABLESPOONS OF PVA GLUE
   INTO A BOWL (MAKE SURE YOU'VE ASKED
   PERMISSION FROM A GROWN-UP FIRST!)

2. ADD ONE OR TWO DROPS OF FOOD
   COLOURING

3. MIX WELL TO DISTRIBUTE THE COLOUR
   EVENLY

4. ADD APPROX. 6 TABLESPOONS OF TALCUM
   POWDER/BABY POWDER

5. PLAY WITH YOUR SLIME!

MON 11TH

TUES 12TH

WEDS 13TH

THURS 14TH

FRI 15TH

SAT 16TH

SUN 17TH

ACTIVITY:

FILL IN THE EMPTY BOXES SO THAT EACH
PICTURE APPEARS ONLY ONCE IN EACH ROW,
COLUMN AND 3X3 BOX. SOLUTION ON PAGE 120.

MON 18TH

TUES 19TH

WEDS 20TH

THURS 21ST

FRI 22ND

SAT 23RD

SUN 24TH

TOP TOOLS OF THE TRADE

IF YOU WANT TO BE A YOUTUBER, YOU NEED
THE RIGHT GEAR! THESE ARE MY FAVOURITE
GADGETS TO USE WHEN MAKING VIDEOS

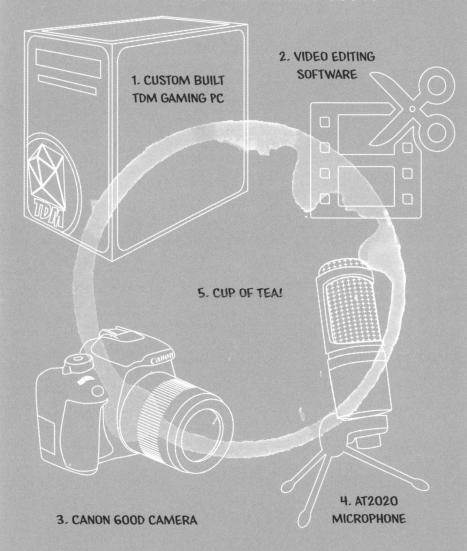

1. CUSTOM BUILT
TDM GAMING PC

2. VIDEO EDITING
SOFTWARE

5. CUP OF TEA!

3. CANON 600D CAMERA

4. AT2020
MICROPHONE

MON 25TH

TUES 26TH

WEDS 27TH

THURS 28TH

FRI 29TH

SAT 30TH

SUN 1ST OCTOBER

DAN  TDM

CODEBREAKER

CAN YOU CRACK THE CODE? USE THE TABLE AND COMPLETE
THE SUMS TO TRANSLATE MY SECRET MESSAGE!
ANSWER ON PAGE 120.

TABLE:

★	10	£	9	@	1	€	5	□	4
A	B	C	D	E	F	G	H	I	J

→	2	#	7	◆	12	✔	8	♥	3
K	L	M	N	O	P	Q	R	S	T

❖	11	¥	6	$	13
U	V	W	X	Y	Z

¥100÷20=? ★ 99÷33=?

$ @ ★ 30-22=?   30-21=? □ 51-42=?

□   ♥ 99÷33=? ★ 88-80=? 150÷50=?

#$ $ ◆❖52-49=? ❖1000÷100=? @

£ 250÷50=? ★ 140÷20=? 40-33=? @ 2

MON 2ND

TUES 3RD

WEDS 4TH

THURS 5TH

FRI 6TH

SAT 7TH

SUN 8TH

MON 9TH

TUES 10TH

WEDS 11TH

THURS 12TH

FRI 13TH

SAT 14TH

SUN 15TH

DENTON

FULL NAME:
DENTON

DATE OF BIRTH:
UNKNOWN

BEST FRIEND:
FIN THE ELF

ENEMY:
DANTDM AND
DR. TRAYAURUS

OCCUPATION:
EVIL OVERLORD

**FAVOURITE
EXPERIMENT:**
THE TIME I CREATED
THE GIANT CLONES!

FAVOURITE HOBBY:
MASTERMINDING EVIL SCHEMES

WORST EXPERIMENT:
NONE OF MY EXPERIMENTS EVER FAIL
(UNLIKE TRAYAURUS!)

**IF YOU WEREN'T AN EVIL
VILLAIN, YOU'D BE:**
A PROFESSIONAL ONLINE TROLL

MON 16TH

TUES 17TH

WEDS 18TH

THURS 19TH

FRI 20TH

SAT 21ST

SUN 22ND

ACTIVITY: DOT-TO-DOT

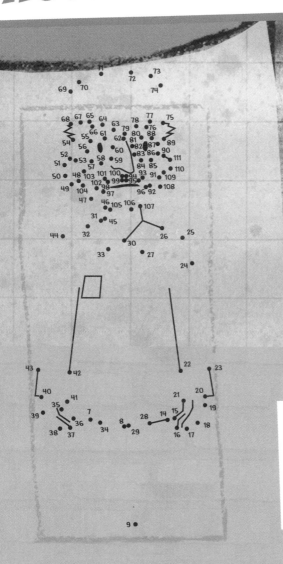

JOIN THE DOTS TO
REVEAL WHO IS
LURKING INSIDE THE
CLONING MACHINE

MON 23RD NEW ZEALAND LABOUR DAY

TUES 24TH

WEDS 25TH

THURS 26TH

FRI 27TH

SAT 28TH

SUN 29TH

HALLOWEEN!

IT'S THE SCARIEST TIME OF YEAR,
AND WHAT'S MORE TERRIFYING THAN FINDING
DENTON ON YOUR DOORSTOP! SCARE AWAY THE
GHOSTS AND GHOULS BY CARVING YOUR VERY
OWN DENTON ONTO THE FACE OF A PUMPKIN.

YOU WILL NEED:

A PUMPKIN   CANDLE
CARDBOARD FOR STENCIL   SCISSORS
SHARP KNIFE   A RESPONSIBLE ADULT

1. DRAW DENTON'S FACIAL FEATURES ONTO THE CARD -- DON'T
   FORGET HIS MONOBROW AND BIG NOSE -- AND GET YOUR
   RESPONSIBLE ADULT TO CUT IT OUT WITH SHARP KNIFE

2. ASK YOUR ADULT TO CUT THE TOP OFF
   THE PUMPKIN, MAKING SURE YOU KEEP THE LID

3. SCOOP OUT AND DISCARD THE FLESH INSIDE OF THE PUMPKIN

4. GET YOUR ADULT TO CUT AROUND THE DENTON STENCIL ON
   THE PUMPKIN WITH A SHARP KNIFE

5. INSERT CANDLE, AND PREPARE
   TO BE TERRIFIED!

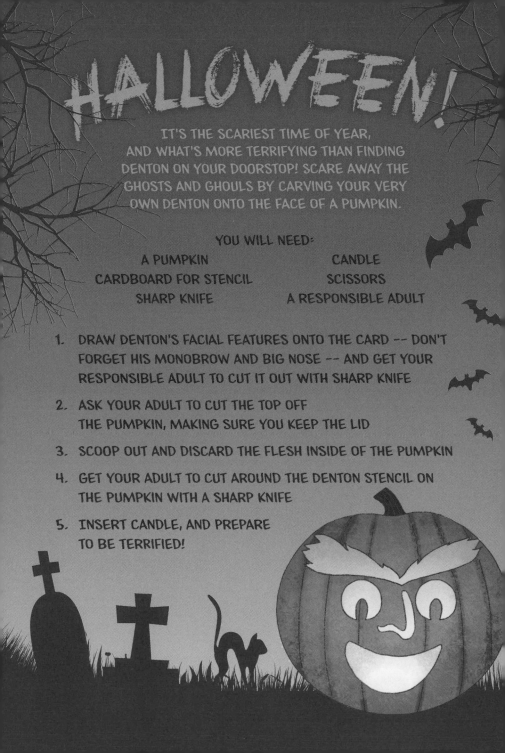

MON 30TH

TUES 31ST HALLOWEEN

WEDS 1ST NOVEMBER

THURS 2ND

FRI 3RD

SAT 4TH

SUN 5TH BONFIRE NIGHT

IT'S DAN'S BIRTHDAY!

HEY GUYS, I'M SUPER EXCITED AS IT'S MY BIRTHDAY! I JUST
LOVE BIRTHDAY CAKE AND HOPE I GET ONE LIKE THE ONE BELOW.
COLOUR IN THE SCENE AND TWEET ME WITH THE HASHTAG
#HAPPYBIRTHDAYDANTDM AND I MIGHT RETWEET YOU AS A
BIRTHDAY SURPRISE!

MON 6TH

TUES 7TH MELBOURNE CUP DAY (AUSTRALIA)

WEDS 8TH DAN'S BIRTHDAY!

THURS 9TH

FRI 10TH

SAT 11TH

SUN 12TH

OPERATION SAVE TRAYAURUS

DENTON HAS CAPTURED TRAYAURUS AND DAN NEEDS YOUR HELP! COMPLETE THE SUMS BELOW TO REVEAL THE COMBINATION TO THE SAFE WHERE THE KEYS TO THE PRISON ARE KEPT! SOLUTION ON PAGE 120

$$3 \times 3 - 1 =$$
$$25 \div 5 + 12 =$$
$$6 \times 8 \div 12 =$$
$$1 + 3 + 2 - 5 =$$

MON 13TH

TUES 14TH

WEDS 15TH

THURS 16TH

FRI 17TH

SAT 18TH

SUN 19TH

ACTIVITY:
MAKE YOUR OWN EDIBLE, ENCHANTED CRYSTALS!

YOU WILL NEED:

- A WOODEN BBQ SKEWER OR A CLEAN WOODEN CHOPSTICK

- A CLOTHES PEG

- FOOD COLOURING

- 250ML OF WATER

- 250G OF SUGAR

- A TALL, CLEAN NARROW GLASS OR JAR

- A HELPFUL ADULT

METHOD:

1. PEG YOUR WOODEN SKEWER OR CHOPSTICK WITH THE CLOTHES PEG SO THAT IT HANGS DOWN INSIDE THE GLASS AND IS ABOUT 1 INCH (2.5 CM) FROM THE BOTTOM OF THE GLASS. PLACE TO THE SIDE FOR NOW.

2. ENLIST THE ASSISTANCE OF YOUR HELPFUL ADULT FOR THE STEPS THAT FOLLOW!

3. POUR YOUR WATER INTO A SAUCEPAN AND BRING IT TO BOIL.

4. POUR ROUGHLY A QUARTER OF YOUR SUGAR INTO THE BOILING WATER, STIRRING CAREFULLY UNTIL IT DISSOLVES.

5. ADD A FEW DROPS OF FOOD COLOURING, IF YOU WANT YOUR CRYSTALS TO BE COLOURFUL.

6. KEEP ADDING MORE AND MORE SUGAR, CONTINUING TO STIR UNTIL IT DISSOLVES. THIS MIGHT TAKE SOME TIME AND PATIENCE!

7. WHEN NO MORE SUGAR WILL DISSOLVE, REMOVE THE PAN FROM THE HEAT AND ALLOW IT TO COOL FOR AT LEAST 20 MINUTES.

8. AFTER APPROX. 20 MINUTES, ASK YOUR ADULT TO CAREFULLY POUR THE SUGAR SOLUTION INTO THE GLASS OR JAR, ALMOST TO THE TOP (THIS IS BEST DONE OVER A SINK!).

9. BALANCE YOUR PEG AND SKEWER IN THE GLASS, MAKING SURE TO AVOID TOUCHING THE SIDES OR BOTTOM OF THE JAR.

10. PUT YOUR JAR IN A SAFE PLACE SO THAT THEY WON'T GET KNOCKED, OR EXPOSED TO TOO MUCH DUST.

11. CHECK ON YOUR CRYSTALS THE NEXT DAY AND NOTICE HOW THEY ARE STARTING TO FORM ON THE SKEWER.

12. AFTER THREE DAYS OR SO, YOUR CRYSTALS SHOULD BE FORMED AND READY TO EAT!

MON 20TH

_____

TUES 21ST

_____

WEDS 22ND

_____

THURS 23RD

_____

FRI 24TH

_____

SAT 25TH | SUN 26TH

MON 27TH

TUES 28TH

WEDS 29TH

THURS 30TH ST ANDREW'S DAY

FRI 1ST DECEMBER

SAT 2ND

SUN 3RD

Countdown to Christmas

AHH, IT'S DECEMBER, MY FAVOURITE TIME OF YEAR! THE COUNTDOWN TO CHRISTMAS HAS BEGUN, AND IT'S TIME TO GET ORGANISED. BELOW IS WHAT'S ON MY CHRISTMAS LIST THIS YEAR. WRITE WHAT YOU'RE HOPING FOR ALONGSIDE.

DAN'S CHRISTMAS PRESENT WISH LIST

1. NEW SOCKS

2. BLUE HAIR DYE

3. HAMMOCK FOR MY OFFICE

4. A PUG ONESIE

5. A HANDY DIARY!

YOUR CHRISTMAS PRESENT WISH LIST

1. ....

2. ....

3. ....

4. ....

5. ....

MON 4TH

TUES 5TH

WEDS 6TH

THURS 7TH

FRI 8TH

SAT 9TH

SUN 10TH

MON 11TH

TUES 12TH

WEDS 13TH

THURS 14TH

FRI 15TH

SAT 16TH

SUN 17TH

MON 18TH

TUES 19TH

WEDS 20TH

THURS 21ST

FRI 22ND

SAT 23RD

SUN 24TH CHRISTMAS EVE

TRUE OR FALSE?

1. DAN'S FAVOURITE COLOUR IS GREEN

TRUE | FALSE

4. DAN'S FAVOURITE COMPUTER GAME IS WORLD OF WARCRAFT

TRUE | FALSE

2. DR TRAYAURUS'S FAVOURITE FOOD IS SANDWICHES

TRUE | FALSE

5. DENTON'S FAVOURITE HOBBY IS CUDDLING KITTENS

TRUE | FALSE

3. GRIM'S FAVOURITE ACTIVITY IS SWIMMING

TRUE | FALSE

6. IF TRAYAURUS WASN'T A SCIENTIST HE WOULD BE AN ACROBAT

TRUE | FALSE

7. DENTON'S BEST FRIEND IS DANTDM

TRUE | FALSE

9. GRIM'S FAVOURITE DINNER IS COOKED CHICKEN

TRUE | FALSE

10. DR TRAYAURUS'S FAVOURITE HOBBY IS ICE-SKATING

TRUE | FALSE

8. DAN FIRST STARTED YOUTUBE IN 2012

TRUE | FALSE

ANSWERS ON PAGE 120

Merry Christmas!

HAPPY CHRISTMAS GUYS! I HOPE YOU HAVE A WONDERFUL DAY, AND THAT YOU RECEIVED EVERYTHING YOU WISHED FOR.

I CAN'T BELIEVE THE YEAR IS NEARLY OVER -- WHAT A CRAZY TIME IT'S BEEN! I HOPE YOU'VE HAD THE BEST YEAR TOO, AND THAT YOU'VE ENJOYED USING THIS DIARY AND COMPLETING ALL THE GAMES, PUZZLES AND EXPERIMENTS.

THANK YOU FOR WATCHING MY VIDEOS AND SUPPORTING EVERYTHING I DO. IT REALLY MEANS A LOT. SEE YOU IN 2018!

MON 25TH CHRISTMAS DAY

TUES 26TH BOXING DAY

WEDS 27TH

THURS 28TH

FRI 29TH

SAT 30TH

SUN 31ST NEW YEAR'S EVE

CAN YOU FIND THE TEN DIFFERENCES BETWEEN THE TWO CHRISTMAS SCENES? ANSWERS ON PAGE 120

NEW YEAR'S RESOLUTIONS

RIGHT, IT'S TIME TO CHECK HOW WELL YOU'VE DONE. FLICK BACK TO PAGE 10 TO SEE THE NEW YEAR'S RESOLUTIONS YOU MADE AT THE START OF THE YEAR. HOW DID YOU DO? WRITE DOWN ANY YOU DIDN'T COMPLETE, AND START YOUR LIST FOR 2018

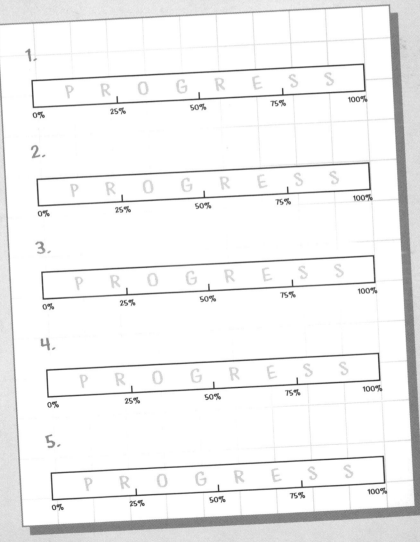

1.

PROGRESS

0%   25%   50%   75%   100%

2.

PROGRESS

0%   25%   50%   75%   100%

3.

PROGRESS

0%   25%   50%   75%   100%

4.

PROGRESS

0%   25%   50%   75%   100%

5.

PROGRESS

0%   25%   50%   75%   100%

MON 1ST NEW YEAR'S DAY

TUES 2ND

WEDS 3RD

THURS 4TH

FRI 5TH

SAT 6TH

SUN 7TH

2018 YEAR PLANNER

JANUARY

SU	MO	TU	WE	TH	FR	SA
	1	2	3	4	5	6
7	8	9	10	11	12	13
14	15	16	17	18	19	20
21	22	23	24	25	26	27
28	29	30	31			

FEBRUARY

SU	MO	TU	WE	TH	FR	SA
				1	2	3
4	5	6	7	8	9	10
11	12	13	14	15	16	17
18	19	20	21	22	23	24
25	26	27	28			

MARCH

SU	MO	TU	WE	TH	FR	SA
				1	2	3
4	5	6	7	8	9	10
11	12	13	14	15	16	17
18	19	20	21	22	23	24
25	26	27	28	29	30	31

APRIL

SU	MO	TU	WE	TH	FR	SA
1	2	3	4	5	6	7
8	9	10	11	12	13	14
15	16	17	18	19	20	21
22	23	24	25	26	27	28
29	30					

MAY

SU	MO	TU	WE	TH	FR	SA
		1	2	3	4	5
6	7	8	9	10	11	12
13	14	15	16	17	18	19
20	21	22	23	24	25	26
27	28	29	30	31		

JUNE

SU	MO	TU	WE	TH	FR	SA
					1	2
3	4	5	6	7	8	9
10	11	12	13	14	15	16
17	18	19	20	21	22	23
24	25	26	27	28	29	30

JULY

SU	MO	TU	WE	TH	FR	SA
1	2	3	4	5	6	7
8	9	10	11	12	13	14
15	16	17	18	19	20	21
22	23	24	25	26	27	28
29	30	31				

AUGUST

SU	MO	TU	WE	TH	FR	SA
			1	2	3	4
5	6	7	8	9	10	11
12	13	14	15	16	17	18
19	20	21	22	23	24	25
26	27	28	29	30	31	

SEPTEMBER

SU	MO	TU	WE	TH	FR	SA
						1
2	3	4	5	6	7	8
9	10	11	12	13	14	15
16	17	18	19	20	21	22
23	24	25	26	27	28	29
30						

OCTOBER

SU	MO	TU	WE	TH	FR	SA
	1	2	3	4	5	6
7	8	9	10	11	12	13
14	15	16	17	18	19	20
21	22	23	24	25	26	27
28	29	30	31			

NOVEMBER

SU	MO	TU	WE	TH	FR	SA
				1	2	3
4	5	6	7	8	9	10
11	12	13	14	15	16	17
18	19	20	21	22	23	24
25	26	27	28	29	30	

DECEMBER

SU	MO	TU	WE	TH	FR	SA
						1
2	3	4	5	6	7	8
9	10	11	12	13	14	15
16	17	18	19	20	21	22
23	24	25	26	27	28	29
30	31					

ANSWERS

WORDSEARCH 1

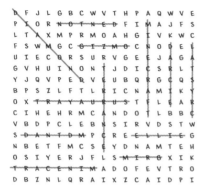

DOT TO DOT 1

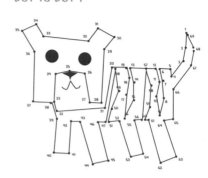

MAZE

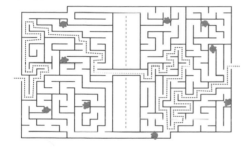

CROSSWORD SOLUTION

ACROSS:
3. TRAYAURUS
4. EXPERIMENT
7. MINECRAFT
8. DENTON

DOWN:
1. YOUTUBE
2. LABORATORY
5. PIG
6. DIAMOND

SPOT THE DIFFERENCE 1

WORDSEARCH 2

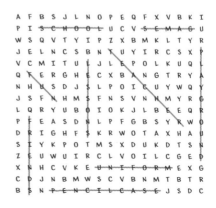

ANSWERS

PICTURE SUDOKU

DOT TO DOT 2

SUDOKU

9	4	7	2	6	8	1	5	3
8	1	5	4	3	7	6	2	9
2	6	3	9	5	1	4	8	7
1	3	2	7	8	4	5	9	6
6	5	4	3	9	2	8	7	1
7	8	9	6	1	5	2	3	4
3	9	1	5	2	6	7	4	8
5	7	8	1	4	3	9	6	2
4	2	6	8	7	9	3	1	5

CODEBREAKER ANSWER

**WHAT YEAR DID I START MY
YOUTUBE CHANNEL**

OPERATION SAVE TRAYAURUS

8 17 4 1

TRUE OR FALSE:
**1: F 2: F 3: F 4: F 5: F
6: F 7: T 8: T 9: F 10: F**

DOT TO DOT 3

CHRISTMAS SPOT THE DIFFERENCE